NOBLE LADY

Noble Lady

The Life of St. Helen

WRITTEN AND ILLUSTRATED
BY THE
DAUGHTERS OF ST. PAUL

ST. PAUL EDITIONS

NIHIL OBSTAT:

    Rt. Rev. John G. Hogan

    Diocesan Censor

IMPRIMATUR:

    ✠ *Richard Cardinal Cushing*

      Archbishop of Boston

July 20, 1966

CONTENTS

Part 1

*"Before every human heart
that has ever beat out
its allotted measures,
the dare of goals as high as God Himself
was tossed down: to be accepted or
to be fled from in terror."*

My Way of Life

PRINCESS AND THE SOLDIER

They came one day on ships, and then tramped across the land everywhere, through fields and paths, dirt roads and hills. Even the peasants of such a remote country as Britain recognized them as legions of Roman soldiers.

It was never an easy thing to see one's country changed into a mere "province" of another more powerful empire. But there was very little friction under the circumstances. . . .

Native customs were still flourishing and, in fact, the east coast of Britain was ruled by the native prince, King Coel. Colchester, where the King lived, was a beautiful little city perched atop a hill. The Romans, with their advanced culture, sniffed and even scoffed a little at this nation of some-what plain people. But they admired them just the same . . . their wholesomeness, their steadfastness.

The camp of the Roman army was pitched just outside of Colchester. Frequently the offi-

13

cers were guests at the castle of King Coel, and guests at his table, for the kindly man understood the discomfort of being away from home.

Captain Constantius Chlorus, tall and muscular, walked briskly down the castle corridor. He was late for dinner with the King, and his brow was furrowed from thought.

"Well, if the Emperor hears of it, the worst that he'll do is send me into exile. Come to think of it, Britain is about as far away from Rome as you can get. I guess I'm in exile already," he laughed to himself.

●

He almost bumped into her, but something made him look up just in time. She had stopped and was smiling at him.

"You look so awfully serious, uh, 'Captain,' is it?"

He shook his head "yes." He was staring at her, and for some ridiculous reason he was blushing. She wore a plain white dress, gathered at the waist by a sash, and falling to the ankles. Her eyes were blue, blue as a Roman sky on a cloudless day. And her sandy-blond hair fell casually down her back.

"What is your name?" he asked questioningly.

"Helen," was the reply.

"But *who* are you?" he insisted.

"*But who are you?*" she asked, obviously joking with him because of his forwardness.

"Constantius Chlorus, Captain in the Roman army, Madam," he answered quite naturally.

At last the island of Britain was beginning to look more interesting. She was walking, now, in the same direction as the banquet hall.

"But who are you?" he kept insisting. They arrived at the entrance to the great hall. She stopped and looked at him.

"You're late, Captain," she said kindly, "and so am I. We have kept the royal party waiting." The court chamberlain greeted them, escorting them to the King's presence. The white-haired King smiled.

"What have you been up to, my daughter?"

"Captain Constantius Chlorus was unavoidably late for the dinner, father, so I rescued him."

They all laughed as Helen and the captain took their proper places at table.

❋

The days turned into weeks and the weeks to months. King Coel had published the date of the wedding. The Princess and the Captain were a well-matched couple. Helen loved his impetuous enthusiasm and joyful heart; Constantius loved her charming simplicity and unpretentious ways. There wasn't a woman in Rome, able to be her equal.

They were married in all the pomp and splendor that King Coel could possibly lavish upon his only daughter. The marriage ceremony itself was quite simple, but it seemed that every citizen of Colchester had come to wish them well.

She was startling in white and Constantius remembered that it was precisely white that she had been wearing the first day that they had met. And of all the unpredictable things, tears were flooding his eyes.

"Helen," he said softly, and smiling, she squeezed his hand the way she always did when she couldn't think of what to say.

Helen was soon to leave the house of her father, a palace none-the-less, and become the wife of a Roman army Captain. She looked up at Constantius and smiled. She liked the idea.

FAMILY ON THE MOVE

As the young captain rose up the ladder of military success, Helen found herself in the background, no longer Princess Helen, but just the wife of "General" Constantius Chlorus. They lived in an army camp now, with five or six other military officers and their families. Sometimes when Constantius was away, Helen would feel like talking to one of the other army wives, just to relieve the loneliness a bit. But no, she would not give in to idle sympathizing, that came so easy to her. And instead of talking to curious neighbors, she would go out and work in her garden. There was something calming and majestic about flower gardens well cared for. And if done well, even gardening is truly an art.

When the young General returned from his campaigns, he would relive his military adventures with Helen. She penetrated his tactics and rejoiced in his victories. And he loved her for it.

Nine years of roaming up and down the province for this vagabond family, and then Helen gave birth to their only child. Constantius was beside himself with joy, for their baby was a son. "Constantine," they called him.

The months slipped by in such a sly manner that Constantine was soon toddling about and getting into everything. Helen followed at his heels.

"No, no, son," she would shriek, pulling a prize vase from his hand.

Constantius had hired plenty of help to aid Helen in running the household. But for Constantine's upbringing, she was personal directress. They were unusually close, this mother and son, and the boy resembled his father more and more; the same dark curly hair and flashing black eyes.

*

Constantius already invisioned a great military career for his only son. He hired the best trainer in fighting tactics. That was for when the boy was older. Constantine, with little effort, excelled in athletics and the various games taught him. And many an afternoon, Helen stood by watching him.

When he did well, he would turn to Helen and she would smile in warm approval. Then he would plunge in again, with even more zeal, because she was pleased with him.

*

Constantius and his family never even guessed that the crowning of a new emperor would have such a direct consequence on their own lives. But, what consequences it did have....

A distinguished looking dispatcher ran up the path, and stopped breathless at Constantius' door. The letter was securely sealed and the Emperor's insignia was quite evident.

The letter may have said many more things, but the essence of it all was this: The new Emperor, Maximian, was summoning Constantius to Rome to receive a new assignment. It was obviously a promotion, and he was to leave as soon as possible.

Helen was stunned, yet thrilled. ... She would be lonely without him, and yet if he did not go to Rome, he would not advance in the career he loved so much. She was holding up wonderfully well ... ordering the servants here and there, arranging everything to perfection. So efficient, did she never tire?

The hours ticked far into the night, yet the Chlorus household was still well lit. Things were pretty well prepared for the voyage so Constantius and Helen went out into the warm night air and talked for hours. The boat was to sail about noon the next day, and time was so short, so terribly short.

"You tell Constantine," Constantius said huskily. "I can't."

"I will tell him." Helen replied. "Don't look so glum, Constantius; you will find out your new appointment and then return home. It won't take long . . . and we'll be waiting here, Constantine and I."

❖

The carriage rode swiftly to the dock. They were a little late, so after a few hasty goodbyes, Constantius was on the ship.

It was only a comparatively short journey. Why were they feeling the separation so much? Constantius stood on the ship's deck. There were many people waving from the shore, but the General was aware of only two figures, a dark-haired impetuous lad of ten years, and a beautiful woman at his side. Only then did it dawn on him that she was wearing a white dress that day, and he remembered that twenty years had passed since they first met.

Helen just stared at the figure on the deck
until the boat blended into the horizon.

She wanted to cry as the ship raised anchor and slowly moved out to sea. She wanted to cry, but she would not. . . . Helen just stared at the now almost invisible figure on the deck until the boat blended into the horizon.

How long she stood there after the boat disappeared, Helen did not know—perhaps only one minute, perhaps more. She felt a hand clasp on her wrist.

"Don't worry, *Helen*, you still have me."

Princess Helen was startled back to reality by the voice of her little boy.

"Son," she said sternly, "you must call me 'mother'."

"Oh," Constantine said, and added pensively, "I am just taking Dad's place until he comes home."

EXILE IN BLACK

The days were growing unusually long, as they always did when Constantius was away, even though there were so many different ways to keep busy.

But above all, the endless questions from Constantine:

"How far is Rome?"

"How long does it take to get there?"

"What's Dad doing there?"

"When will he be home?"

"How soon?"

And the litany was growing and growing. Always with patience his mother answered and it helped to relieve the loneliness a little. A year and more ticked by.

She was sitting in the garden one afternoon, embroidering some linen, when an official dispatcher of the Emperor hastened up the path. Helen knew his face; she had seen him a few times before when Constantius had been home.

"Princess Helen," he was shaking visibly, and his face was a ghostly white. Instinctively she threw aside her sewing and stood up.

"What is it, sir?"

"Princess Helen," he stammered, "I have a message for you."

"What is it?" she demanded. "Stop all this stalling!"

His voice would not expend itself. Sorry for her impatience, she asked softly,

"Tell me, soldier, what is it?"

"The essence of the message is this: The new Emperor, Maximian, has appointed Constantius his 'Caesar' or assistant, to help govern the Western part of the Empire."

Helen's eyes shone with joy as the man spoke.

"The new Caesar will govern Britain, Gaul and Spain," he continued.

"Then Constantius will be coming home soon?" The excitement was mounting.

"Yes, but he is not coming alone," he stammered. "There was one condition to General Constantius' appointment as Caesar. Maximian insisted that he marry Theodora, Maximian's step-daughter. One does not say 'no' too easily to old Maximian, Princess. The divorce was granted quickly. Constantius and Theodora are already married." His voice was shaking and stumbling. "They will arrive here in less than two months time."

"I must go away," she said, stunned.

"And Constantine must stay here by his father's orders," the man said gently.

"I must go alone . . ." she said.

*

The next few days were spent in preparing to leave for her new home, although it would not be much like home. She would be leaving for Treves, her place of "exile," without even seeing Constantius, and above all, without her son.

Helen forced herself to be realistic. There was a reason for it all, though for her there was no reason good enough.

Everything was prepared. She would be traveling quietly, without a lot of pomp, for there was not much honor in being a "repudiated wife." Nor did it impress Imperial Rome that Helen was the daughter of the late territorial monarch, Coel, from the "back woods" of Britain.

The time had arrived to tell Constantine. By now he knew that something was wrong, but never did he imagine what!

"I wish I had an ounce of courage," Helen thought, "just an ounce."

They had a long conversation—just mother and son.

"Some day I will make it up to you, Mother," Constantine said, "I swear it."

The next morning dawned clear and crisp. Long before Constantine was awake, Helen was on her way.

Constantius and Theodora arrived in York some time later.

✻

A few years passed. Diocletian who succeeded the Emperor Maximian, ordered the youthful Constantine to Rome, so that he could be closer to the Emperor's wrath in case the capable Constantius proved to be unfaithful. Away from his mother and Britain, these were to be the most lonely years of his life. As Constantine emerged into manhood, he went on many campaigns and put into use his soldiering skills. In fact, the Emperor sent him on several dangerous missions, in the hope that the promising young soldier would be killed, but it wasn't working. And the jealousy of the Emperor mounted daily.

Years were passing and the Emperor's wrath was mounting. At last he decided to

They had a long conversation
— just mother and son.

send Constantine back to Britain, figuring that it was less dangerous to have such a clever man back in York, rather than within the walls of the Emperor's palace.

Constantine sailed for Britain.

*

Could it be possible that thirteen years had passed since the mysterious Lady moved to Treves? She lived in a lovely house, yet no distinguished visitors ever came to call. She was very beautiful still, and had such a gracious way, and yet no one was able to crash the barrier of her background. Speculation ran high around Treves as to who the kindly lady was, and yet no one really knew.

Princess Helen kept to herself as much as possible. Yet she was not divorced from the world totally. She would ask about current events and kept abreast, especially on the situation of the religious sect, who called themselves "Christian." Often she would question one of her servants who seemed to share her same interest in them.

Such a wonderfully pure doctrine was that taught by Jesus. Love of neighbor as the proof of love for God; humility, purity, the dignity of man . . . these were just a few of the principles it upheld.

And did the Christians deserve to be persecuted for these beliefs? Helen was ashamed that even in Britain the edict against them was being so forcefully enacted. She could have remained indifferent about the whole situation. After all, she was not a Christian. The battle was not her own. She had no obligation whatso-ever, to help them. Nor did they ever suspect that she could.

Helen knew of one man who definitely could help the situation. He was the Caesar of Britain and resided in York. Constantius Chlorus was his name.

The battle was her own pride now.

What if she went to his palace and was utterly scorned by him? What if the luring Theodora laughed in her face?

"I can't do it," Helen thought.

"And yet," she added, "what if he does welcome me? What if he does listen to me? Perhaps he will revoke the infamous edict. I must go . . . it is my duty to go."

"But, my lady, so soon, tomorrow morning? We can never be ready," her servant stuttered nervously.

"'Course we'll be ready!" Helen exclaimed. "The two of us will be there. Get a good sturdy carriage."

"But, my lady . . ."

"Begin packing instantly," she commanded, "or for sure we won't be ready in the morning."

A TEMPORARY REUNION

It was the year 306. The co-emperors, Maximian and Diocletian, had retired into the background and Constantius Chlorus and Maxentius succeeded to the throne. This was in reality the great dream of Constantius' life. As the impact of the news hit him, memories of past years toyed in his mind. He had given up his wife and son with an eye cast on his distant dream of some day ruling the great Roman Empire. Why, he had even given up his peace of mind and wrestled steadily with a guilty conscience. But no one knew. He had everything he wanted now, and still the loneliness was so profound.

In the quiet of his room, Constantius, with his hands clasped behind his back, paced the floor with rhythmic step.... If only there was someone who knew and understood. Theodora didn't; not that she didn't want to, of course, but she didn't have the intelligence or fineness of spirit to penetrate a man's heart.

"Helen would understand," he said out loud. How often had he mumbled that phrase over the years. He stared in the mirror and the reflection was not a pleasant sight. His hair was streaked with grey; and his shoulders were decidedly rounded.

"Constantius, you are old," he muttered sullenly.

*

"The Princess Helen to see your Excellency," the man announced. Constantius stared in disbelief.

"I will see her at once," he found himself saying. "Make sure we are not interrupted for any reason!"

He walked to the room where she was waiting. He stayed outside the door for a few moments, trying to collect his thoughts.

She stood as the old man entered the room.

"Constantius," she said shakily, "is it you?"

He smiled. It was his smile . . . and tears rushed to Helen's eyes. Constantius took both of her hands in his own.

"How many years, Helen, how long has it been?"

"Thirteen years since you went to Rome, Constantius."

"Thirteen years you have been in Treves . . . ," he paused, and then continued, "the victory was *not* mine, Helen. What I'm trying to say is, I was wrong."

"But, what about Theodora?"

"I have never loved her," he stated flatly.

There was no bitterness in Helen. The years of quiet suffering had been miraculously lifted in these few moments of conversation.

"You must stay here now, Helen, in the guest house, and await your son."

"Constantine — here?" Helen cried.

"He is already sailing from Rome," Constantius assured her.

There was a moment's silence.

"I have not come just for my own consolation, Constantius," Helen said, smiling a bit. "There's something else on my mind."

"Of course there is." Constantius laughed. "Your mind is as keen as ever. What is it?"

Helen grew earnest.

"The edict against the poor Christians," she said, "you can revoke it, Constantius. You are not just the 'Caesar' now. You are the 'Emperor'."

"And would you be a Christian too?" he asked.

"No," she said softly, "but I like their God and I like their doctrine of love. You must,

Constantius; you have to revoke that edict. It is not just."

"I don't agree with that edict any more than you do. It's senseless. Now that Diocletian is out of the way, it will cease. I will publish the revocation at once!" Then his brow wrinkled, as he said quietly,

"Constantine does not know yet that I am the Emperor. Things are happening much too fast, Helen. But I will never survive a trip to Rome. The doctors say I don't have long to live."

＊

In the days that followed, Constantius grew steadily weaker. His fever mounted higher and higher. He called Helen's name continually and clutched her hand, making sure that she was still at his side. When the fever subsided, Constantius begged to see Constantine, his son.

"But his ship has not arrived yet. As soon as he arrives you shall see him," Helen assured Constantius. She was frantic. The ship was overdue but heaven only knew the weather conditions.

The days dragged endlessly by. At last the ship docked. As the passengers filed to shore, a tall broad shouldered Roman officer gazed about, wondering whom his father had delegated to meet him.

Helen pushed her way through the crowd. She had spotted him.

"Constantine," she called.

"Mother," he said, dumbfounded, "it can't be."

"Oh yes it is," she said softly, as he scooped her into his arms.

They walked arm in arm toward the carriage, both talking at once, yet each grasping what the other was saying. As they sat in the back of the carriage, Helen explained Constantius' serious condition, to prepare her son for the tremendous physical relapse that had occurred.

The joy on old Constantius' face meant everything to mother and son, as they walked into his room. The persistent fever and pain had distorted his features, almost beyond recognition. Constantine stood in mute silence.

"My son," Constantius struggled to lift his head a little, "I have waited for you to come. So often I thought you wouldn't make it on time. Son, I have something for you," he said.

"What is it?" Constantine smiled, puzzled a little.

"The Roman Empire," he replied.

Within a week Constantius was dead.

CONSTANTINE

The shoes that his father had left him, were soon to be outgrown by his leader-son, Constantine. Spontaneously, the legions of soldiers proclaimed him the "new Emperor." Of course there were other claims to the imperial throne. For example, Maxentius, the proud, immoral man, who had set his headquarters in Rome. But he didn't forget Constantine, who was in far-off Britain. In fact, he had even picked out another wife for him. The lady in question was none other than the beautiful Fausta, his young daughter. For reasons of politics, Constantine did as his father before him had done. He divorced his peasant-wife and married the lovely lady. Perhaps there was only one person in the world who understood the loneliness in the heart of Constantine's first wife. Helen soothed the pain as much as she could, and yet there were no words, really, that she could say.

But a look of reproach was enough for Constantine—and he had no answer. All the excuses sounded so feeble next to the cold, even stare of his mother's gaze.

"I had to, Mother . . . ," his eyes were blazing. "Things are just that way. I didn't want it to be, but. . . ."

Helen turned quickly and left the room.

❀

Constantine was growing more powerful politically each day. He had the firm support of the legions of Britain, Gaul and Spain. However, the security of the western part of the Empire was not yet his. There was a way, of course, to win. It meant defeating Maxentius, once and for all. It meant going to Rome; fighting him on Roman ground, which seemed almost sacrilegious.

Constantine began the tedious task of transporting his troops to Roman soil. The journey was a long and arduous one, partly by sea, partly by land. It even meant crossing the great Alp mountains, as Hannibal had done five hundred years earlier. And yet there was a reason for it all. Perhaps many motives crossed through Constantine's mind; a little bit of love for power; and a desire to lay a great success at the feet of Helen—and Fausta. But there were far more noble reasons too—his love for Rome. Rome needed a wise leader to preserve her culture and her glorious past. And she needed a leader who would insure justice for all of her citizens. Maxentius would do none of those things, nor was he even capable of them. He was a small man with an equally small mentality and Constantine felt it his duty to crush him into obscurity.

Victories at Turin and Verona, lent a bit of optimism on Constantine's bazaar plan, and yet, there could be no complacency. Constantine and his army began the march to Rome where Maxentius waited with his main forces. Constantine's men were outnumbered three to one.

The armies met by the Milvian Bridge, barely two miles outside of Rome. It was the year 312 . . . a memorable year. The day preceding the battle, about noon, Constantine saw a brilliant light in the sky, shaped like a cross.

"By this sign you will conquer," a voice said.

With the tension of the anticipated battle, and the strain of previous ones, Constantine, alone in his tent, put his head in his hands, and thought. . . .

"What does it mean . . . that cross?" he asked himself again and again.

Then he suddenly recalled his mother telling him about that curious sect, who called

themselves Christians. Wasn't their symbol
the cross?

"Yes," he was saying aloud, "their doctrine
is strange enough—a God, Who became a man,
born of a virgin, crucified upon the hard wood
of Calvary's cross. . . . That was the story, wasn't
it? Then the cross must be a symbol of the God
of the Christians." And he repeated the words
again.

"In this sign you will conquer."

"Perhaps victory lies with the God of the
Christians," Constantine said pensively. And he
began dictating an incredible command:

"A white cross is to be painted on the hel-
met and shield of every man in my army, as
well as on the pennants and standards."

"As crews of painters began slapping criss-
cross white lines on just about everything in
sight, the curiosity of the soldiers mounted.
Only about one tenth of the army knew the se-
cret of the magical emblem, for only one tenth
of the army was Christian. They were delirious
with joy. Rumors sped through the different
legions that Constantine had already been
baptized. The word came too, that if Constantine won this battle of the Milvian Bridge, the
Christian sect would definitely be freed from
the bonds of persecution once and for all. And

it seems that this is one time that rumors might just come true. . . .

The battle raged for hours. Heavy casualties resulted on both sides, but Constantine's army, with white painted crosses, slashed through the enemy and won a decisive victory. Even the sly Maxentius died in the battle.

The Roman Senate built an arch of Triumph in Rome to celebrate his victory and Constantine's claim on the West was sealed. But the real victory could be claimed by Someone else; that marvelous God, who became a man; the God of the Christians.

*

She came to Rome to see him. The wirey lady with her now graying hair, demanded to see her son, "instantly." She tapped her cane vigorously on the floor.

Helen was escorted into Constantine's chamber.

"Mother," he said warmly, "I've missed you. There is so much to say. Your home is here now. Everything was being prepared for your arrival. But of course you upset all the plans by arriving too early—the same unpredictable Mother."

She was staring at him all the while, and then she stepped toward him and embraced him.

"You have forgiven me about Fausta, haven't you, Mother?"

"I don't like it a bit," she said, "I will never agree with it, but you are my son."

"Once I told you, Mother, that I would make it up to you for other hurts," Constantine said.

"But I don't want honors now, son, I want something much more."

"What is it?" he asked simply.

"To meet the God of the Christians and to understand His doctrine," she said.

"I have met Him, Mother," the Emperor was saying.

"I know you have met Him, Constantine, and He will use you to spread His wonderful message," Helen said.

"And you will be right with me," he assured. "That is," he smiled broadly, "if you don't scare the Romans away with your new title."

Taking her hand, he announced majestically:

"You shall henceforth be known as 'Domina Flavia Julia Helena Augusta.'"

"I am Constantine's mother," she snapped. "That is the only title I wish to have."

Part 11

*God alone is never sought
in vain,
And when He is sought
with hope,
He is always found.*

St. Bernard

ROME MEETS THE LADY

Three hundred years of suffering and scorn, misunderstanding and contempt ... sometimes less severe, sometimes more severe, and the Christian sect had not only survived, but prospered. There were converts in the most precarious places, not only in ghettos of the cities, but in senate chambers and noble palaces, in the Roman legions and the most learned of classrooms.

The Christ of Galilee had penetrated deeply on Roman soil and the Faith brought to their land by twelve ignorant fishermen, was not dying out. In fact, the doctrine of the Master had reached its final conquest. It had climbed the steps of the Emperor's palace and entered his mind and heart.

A decree was published, Constantine's "Edict of Milan," which would have almost eternal repercussions. Not only was Christianity freed from the tyranny of persecution, but it was recognized as the official Religion of the Empire.

＊

The Empress-Mother herself embraced Christianity and was baptized. All of Rome fell in love with this impetuous little lady. She was 63 years old, but had the enthusiasm of a teenager. Each day she seemed to grow in love for the Faith she had embraced so late in life. But for Helen, life was far from over. There was so much to do—so many more bridges to cross.

Every beggar in Rome had met her personally. Many of them she knew by name. If they were sick, if they were hungry, if they were in need, they came to her, unashamed. Her smile would fill their hearts with a new love for humanity; her alms would fill their hands with a new chance to begin again. And it was never enough. She pushed herself with new effort, each day, to do more.

Constantine made her understand that the treasury of the Empire was at her disposal, and the Empress-Mother dipped into it again and again—now to build a church, another time to remodel one. She built hotels for travelers and homes for the sick. Whether or not the inhabitants could pay, made no difference. Schools were also established for those who wished to be instructed in the Faith.

Helen's mind was on fire, thinking of new ideas to serve Christ better, to make Him better known. Even her physical appearance glowed with a healthy air. She was like a young girl, who had met her life-time love. And yet this was more of a love than anything she had ever, in the by-gone days of youth, shared with Constantius.

"Mother, you must cut down your rigorous schedule," Constantine would plead, "you are killing yourself."

"Oh, nonsense, Constantine," she would scold, "I'm an old lady now, and I've got to make up for a lot of lost time."

"Besides," she would add coyly, "I think I'm old enough to know what I'm doing."

THE ROAD TO JERUSALEM

When one event occurs, who can know the repercussions it will have? An example of this would be the Emperor, Constantine's tremendous victory over Licinius, the ruler of the eastern part of the Empire.

Licinius cracked under the crushing heel of Constantine—another victim of his iron will. Constantine had believed since boyhood days, that Rome, no matter how large, deserved only one ruler. Now, the day had come when he could make his opinion a reality. It was the year 324 A.D. The great Roman Empire, which extended her borders from Britain to Persia, from Germany to Africa, had one sole ruler, the Emperor, Constantine.

*

The Empress-Mother was thinking again.

"Rome is the center of Christianity now," she mused, "but Christianity did not begin here. Could one ask for anything more in life, than to go to Jerusalem, to Nazareth, to Calvary, and see with her own eyes, the places where the Master lived and walked and died?"

"The trip is long and tedious," her thoughts were racing, "and I will soon be seventy-five years old. Can I do it?"

"Oh, if Constantine could read my thoughts," she smiled to herself. "And what of the good to be done there? What of the poor and the suffering? Perhaps even an old fool, like myself, can bring a bit of Christ's joy to them."

✱

"Son, I've got an idea," Helen announced quite casually. "I do hope you won't object. . . ."

"*I know* I will object, Mother. Your ideas are, shall we say, 'startling'?"

She was grinning at Constantine, the way she did when she wanted a favor.

"What is it, Mother?" he asked, with a tone of laughter in his voice.

"I want you to arrange a trip for me."

"To Britain?" he asked puzzled.

"Oh, no," she replied, quickly.

"Then where?" he asked.

"To the Holy Land," Helen replied, trying to be as nonchalant as ever.

Constantine stared at her in disbelief.

"What?" he shouted.

"I must go," Helen continued earnestly. "The Master expects it of me. And do you know something, son? Lately I have been thinking much of the death of Our Lord; of Calvary, the hill where He died. And do you know what else I've been thinking? That if one just has the patience to search long enough, and hard enough, then the cross that He died on may be located."

"But, Mother," Constantine said, trying to be level-headed, "Jesus has been dead for three centuries."

"The time is irrelevant," Helen answered quickly. "The executioners had the habit of burying all the instruments used for such a death, deep into the ground. No doubt it will take a lot of excavating, but we'll find it."

"We must find it," his mother continued. "The world of today needs to remember the center and core of Christianity ... that infamous cross. Today, the word 'Christian' is no longer synonymous with the word 'martyr' or the word 'persecution.' You have made it

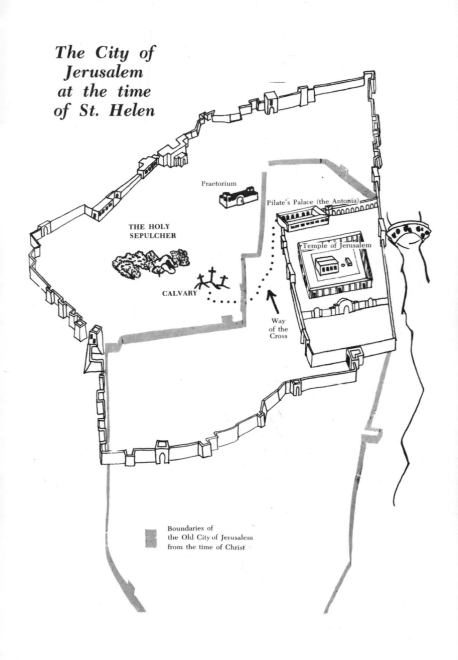

The City of
Jerusalem
at the time
of St. Helen

Praetorium

Pilate's Palace (the Antonia)

THE HOLY
SEPULCHER

Temple of Jerusalem

CALVARY

Way
of the
Cross

Boundaries of
the Old City of Jerusalem
from the time of Christ

easy for men to become Christians, son. Now, we don't want them to forget that being a Christian means suffering. Imagine the impact upon the Christian world to know that the true cross had been located."

"I must be crazy," he muttered to his mother, "but I'll do it. . . . I'll arrange the trip."

●

It would involve an awful lot of protocol, for Helen would travel through the East as the official representative of her Emperor-son. She was dressed in gorgeous gowns and draped in shimmering jewels–and it aggravated her.

"One old woman can certainly cause a lot of trouble," she mused to her ladies in waiting. But for love of Constantine, she would bear with all the "fancy trimmings." Besides, she wanted to see the Holy Land, and whether she dressed as princess or pauper, at this point it made little difference.

The journey was begun. . . .

THE SEARCH

The kindly old Bishop, who waited at Jerusalem's gate for the Empress-Mother, was himself a unique personality, and a holy man besides. He was Macarius, whom we now honor with the word "Saint" before his name. But on this particular day, as the sun beat down mercilessly, and wilted his spirits considerably, Bishop Macarius would have found it hard to believe that he would ever be ranked among the Blessed.

There was the expectation of what was to come, the genuine wondering as to just what the great Helen would be like. Meanwhile, the sun was still beating down, and the Bishop was growing impatient.

"The caravan is approaching now, Your Excellency," his assistant was saying. "Do you see the dust on the distant road?" he asked, as he pointed anxiously ahead. They would be arriving almost two hours later than they had planned, and yet those little unexpected delays are hardly avoidable.

The Bishop found himself immersed in a sea of anxious chatter; animals were screeching, and men of all sizes and types, running about. At last, the beautiful carriage, which carried the Empress, stopped. An efficient little servant helped her out. She found herself face to face with the Bishop of Jerusalem. Thus, two future Saints met.

He liked her instantly. The zesty little old lady was very much worth the wait. Empress Helen was destined to be even more than Bishop Macarius ever anticipated. In fact, many hours during the next few months, he would spend running after, or should we say running to catch up with her.

●

In the days that followed, Helen lost no time tracing her steps to the places where Jesus had been. But the Noble Lady had laid aside her jewels and plush clothes. She was clothed instead, in a plain black dress with a scarf covering her head. Now she was ready for her journey to Calvary.

Traveling by the "Way of Sorrow," Helen, accompanied by the Bishop and a steadily growing crowd of onlookers, crossed the lower town and walked up the steep incline, to the gate of Ephraim. At this point, the city walls formed in an angle. A three-cornered enclosure about twenty yards outside the walls, was their destination. Called the "place of the skull" because of its shape, we know it as "Calvary."

The Empress stared indignantly at the most wretched of sights. Atop one of the most hallowed spots of all Christendom, a temple stood, not dedicated however, to the God Who had died there, but to a fictitious pagan deity, called Venus. An enemy of Christianity, from by-gone years, the Emperor Hadrian, had thought to destroy the despised Christ of Galilee, by defaming the spot where He died.

And now many years later, that same Christ is more alive than ever, and the Emperor's own mother had traveled from Rome to Jerusalem, just to locate the stumps of trees that had once held the Master's tortured limbs.

"We must begin at once, Your Excellency." Helen turned impatiently to Bishop Macarius, "Remove that . . . that . . . 'thing.'"

Mattocks and spades and a variety of other instruments began to appear. The men to work with them soon began pouring up the hill. The preparations were hasty, and yet, amazing-

"Remove   that . . . that . . . 'thing'!"

ly well organized. But this was only the beginning.

The hours became days and the days, weeks. People chuckled at the impetuousness of that marvelous old lady, who would not give up. Venus' temple had long since fallen into obscurity and Calvary Hill looked like a series of giant mole hills, freshly dug.

"But it just isn't there, Lady Helen," the men pleaded with her.

"Dig," she commanded, "dig deeper. It must be there. It *is* there!"

And so they did just what the lady said.

Deeper and deeper into the ground–and the furrows of fresh dirt mounted. Many an hour Helen stood by watching ... hoping ... praying. Her determination was like a vitamin, injected into the tired arms of the workers.

At last a few of the spades cracked against the hard wood.

"Wood!" someone shouted. And the workers centered their activity on that one spot. Slowly, the hidden wood was uncovered. Not just one, but three crosses came into view. Helen stood by in quiet relief. Now only one victory remained; to find out which of the three crosses was the one which had once held the body of Christ.

It was Bishop Macarius, who stepped forward with the solution. He told the Empress of a dying old woman, who lived near by.

"I will have her carried on a stretcher to this very spot," the Bishop said. "We can touch the crosses to her. Which ever is the true one will heal her."

"Bring the dying woman," Helen consented. "In fact, perhaps it would even be better to go to her home and accompany her here ourselves."

"Come," the Bishop invited.

The old woman was made as comfortable as possible as young arms carried her stretcher to the scene. Behind the stretcher, led by the Bishop and the Empress, the curious, ever-growing crowd, followed.

They reached the scene of Calvary's hill, just as the sun had slid into the twilight and left trails of pink streams behind. It was cool now, and even the noisy, restless crowd was unusually still.

"Grant, O Lord," the Bishop prayed, "that as soon as the health-giving wood touches this woman, who is lying here near death, that she may be recalled to life from the gates of death. . . ."

The cross was placed
next to the dying woman's stretcher.

The first cross was placed next to the dying woman's stretcher. Helen lifted the invalid's arm gently and touched it to the wood. There were no results. The second cross was brought but it too proved uneventful. When the woman's arm touched the third cross, new life surged through her body. Color flooded her cheeks and her eyes, alert and intelligent, opened. And she was well.

The Empress Helen heaved a sigh of relief, and tears rolled down her cheeks. She embraced the cross that she had sought for so long ... that cross, which had caused her to travel so many miles. She knelt amid the dirt of Calvary Hill and thanked the good God, Who granted such a tremendous consolation to a poor old woman, like herself. And she really meant it. She meant that she was poor in spiritual things; poor in the things that count most with God. She meant that, although she was an Empress to the world of her day, in the eyes of God, perhaps she was far less than the beggar in the market place.

EMPRESS ANGEL

All of Jerusalem had been touched by the kindness of Empress Helen in one way or the other. Her visit would leave an impression, which would last and last. A beautiful basilica was being constructed on the top of Mount Calvary, but Helen would not stay on to see its completion. A long journey through the East awaited her. After all, she was Constantine's official representative.

And so they were under way—the caravan with its bright imperial colors and the glimmering carriage, where the Empress rode. The crowds followed to the city gate. Many cried without shame. The carriage stopped and Helen got out to say the last "good byes."

"Pray for me, Your Excellency," the Empress said to Bishop Macarius.

"And you. . . ," he said, "you pray for Jerusalem's poor Bishop."

61

❀

Wherever she went, be it the meanest of towns or the most plush of cities, Empress Helen did not leave the town until a church, housing the Blessed Sacrament was under construction, or promised for the near future. Or if the town was fortunate enough to have a church, she would adorn it with a beautiful gift to give the Lord more glory.

❀

There were endless demands made on the generous Empress, but she never refused anyone . . . no, not since she had become a Christian. She was finding out more and more each day, that following Christ means "giving"; giving without stopping.

"There will always be a next time, and a next time, and a next. Oh God, may I always say 'yes.'" That was her prayer. That was the prayer of Helen.

She stopped to help the poor, the sick, the galley slaves, the miners. In fact, once when her caravan stopped for the night, they picked a location near a mine,which had exploded the previous day. Many of the injured men were lying in make-shift tents, moaning. Her party tried to keep the information from Helen, so that she would not worry.

"Who are you?"

During the night, who knows at just what time, the Empress realized that she was awake. She did not wonder why for very long. For soon she became aware of persistent moans, long and painful. The sound was not in her dreams . . . it was real. Exhausted from traveling all day long, she lay awake for a moment, trying to come in contact with reality. But the moaning persisted. Helen sat up in bed and wrapped her fur-trimmed cloak around herself. She slipped into her sandals, and followed the sound. Closer and closer came the voice. A make-shift tent appeared and the light of the moon, revealed an old, wrinkled miner lying beneath it. Stooping down, Helen met the gaze of the dying man.

With feverish eyes, blazing, he cried only one word:

"Water . . . water!"

The Empress retraced her steps back to the imperial tent and found a large pitcher. She filled it with cool water and added a few fresh cut limes. Quickly Helen returned to the miner's tent. She touched the water to his parched lips and let him drink freely. Then she bathed his tortured forehead, patting the water gently to his face. The fever subsided enough to bring the man to his senses.

"Who are you?" he called as the lady was leaving. She turned around and smiled a beautiful, full smile; then she was gone.

"It was the Mother of God," the old man was babbling to the attendant.

"No sir," the attendant replied. "It was *not* the Mother of God, but the mother of the Emperor Constantine."

"The Empress Helen?" he asked, smiling.

"One and the same," the man answered him.

"She came to me," the old miner said in halting words, "a messenger of the Lord. . . . Tell her . . . tell her that because of her, a poor old miner dies a penitent and a Christian."

Macedonia

ROME

MEDITERRANEAN SEA

St. Helen's Journey
to the Holy Land

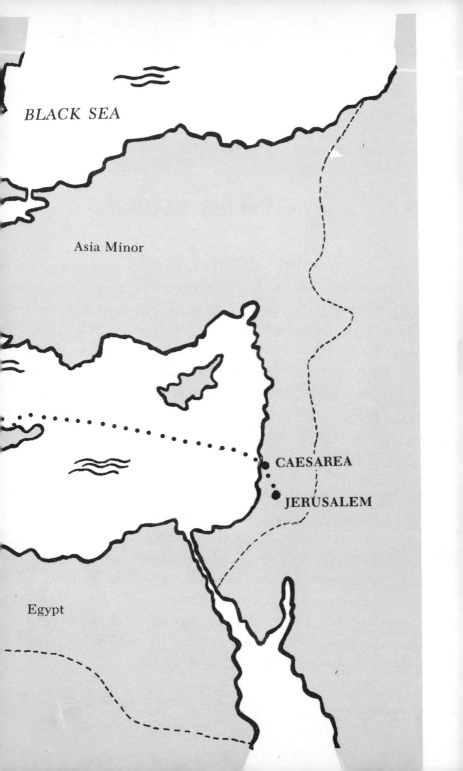

GLORIOUS RETURN

The trip home took months of strenuous travel, much too strenuous for a woman eighty-one years old. And crossing the Adriatic Sea, had been an ordeal, which could have easily defeated a person fifty years younger. In fact at one spot, the storm had been so frightening, that Helen had taken one of the three precious nails, which had been found near the true cross, and tossed it into the sea. The other two, she would take home to her son.

News traveled quickly. All of Rome prepared to greet the Empress-Mother, as she arrived home. Crowds cheered the lady as her carriage rode by, and yet Helen was scarcely aware of it. She had aged considerably, almost beyond recognition. They made her as comfortable as possible in her own suite at the palace. Constantine rushed in to see her. She was awake now, and smiling.

"Mother, are you ever without a smile?" Constantine asked, with tears flooding his cheeks.

"Oh, I am getting too old to smile," Helen laughed. "I really feel old now, son."

"But you are as beautiful as ever," he winked.

"Son," she said impulsively, "you're such an imp! Can an eighty-one year old woman be beautiful?"

"Yes," he said softly, "if she's your mother." He kissed her on the cheek.

"Sleep now . . . and when you wake up, I have many things to tell you."

THE GREATEST JOURNEY

Time did not improve Helen's weakened physical condition. Weeks had passed and the best that she could do was to sit up in bed, propped up by a few pillows. Constantine was spending many more hours by her bedside. He showed her a sample of the coins minted in her honor.

"Oh, Constantine, how foolish," she laughed. "Do you think *that* will make me immortal? Or any of those *silly* titles like, 'Nobilissima Femina'? Imagine me . . . 'Noble Lady!' What next?"

❋

The Empress confessed her sins and received the Holy Eucharist for what was to be the last time. She remained for hours in silence, but with obvious joy on her face and a calmness which brought consolation to all around her.

When God is sought with hope,
He is always found.

❋

It was early morning and the window next to Helen's bed revealed the first streaks of light appearing in the horizon.

"Do you hear the wheels of the carriage, Constantine?" Helen asked feverishly.

"Look," she said, propping herself up on her elbow. "Look at the beautiful carriage—much more beautiful than the one I went to Jerusalem in—and it is coming for me. . . . I am going home, Constantine."

"Home?" he asked, clutching her shoulders, "home to Britain?"

"No, son," she said softly, "home to Heaven."

She reached out for his hand and squeezed it securely. Then she released her grasp. And sleep came . . . the sleep of eternal peace.

DAUGHTERS OF ST. PAUL

50 St. Paul's Ave., Jamaica Plain, BOSTON, MASS. 02130
Telephone number: **617-522-8911; 617-522-0875**

St. Paul Catholic Book and Film Centers

MASSACHUSETTS
Boston, 02111. 172 Tremont St. **617-426-5464**

NEW YORK
Staten Island, 10301. 78 Fort Place; **212-447-5071**
Bronx, 10458. 625 East 187th St.; **212-584-0440**
Buffalo, 14203. 525 Main St.; **716-853-1905**

CONNECTICUT
Bridgeport, 06603. 202 Fairfield Ave.; **203-335-9913**

OHIO
Cleveland, 44115. 2105 Ontario St.
(at Prospect Ave.); **216-621-9427**

PENNSYLVANIA
Philadelphia, 19147. 1127 So. Broad St.;
215-463-4385

FLORIDA
Miami, 33137. 2700 Biscayne Blvd.; **305-371-0835**

LOUISIANA
New Orleans, 70002. 4403 Veterans Memorial
Blvd., Metairie; **504-887-7631**
Alexandria, 71301. 86 Bolton Ave.; **318-443-5952**

TEXAS
San Antonio, 78205. 114 East Main Plaza;
512-224-8101

CALIFORNIA
San Francisco, 94108. 46 Geary St.; **415-781-5180**
Oakland, 94612. 278 17th St.; **415-832-4134**
San Diego, 92101. 1570 Fifth Ave.; **714-232-1442**

CANDADA
Toronto, 395, Ontario. 3022 Dufferin St.

ENGLAND
London, W. 8. 57, Kensington Church St.

AUSTRALIA
Sydney, 2140. 58, Abbotsford Rd.,
Homebush, N.S.W.

PHILIPPINE ISLANDS
Pasay City, Manila. 2650, F.B. Harrison,
P.O. Box 3576

INDIA
Bombay, 50-AS. 143, Waterfield Rd.

AFRICA
Lagos, Nigeria. 35, Jones St., P.O. Box 3243